24,245

Out Of The Earth I Sing

Poetry and Songs of
Primitive Peoples of the World

Edited by Richard Lewis

W · W · NORTON & COMPANY · INC · NEW YORK

Out Of The Earth I Sing

BOOKS BY RICHARD LEWIS

Out of the Earth I Sing

In a Spring Garden

In Praise of Music

Moment of Wonder

Miracles

Moon For What Do You Wait?

Contents

ACKNOWLEDGMENTS

The editor wishes to express his gratitude to the following publishers and authors for permission to include material in this anthology from their original publications.

"Dance of the Animals," from *The African Saga*, by Blaise Cendras. Repinted with the permission of Harcourt, Brace and World.

"Paddling Song," from *African Song Sampler*, published by the Cooperative Recreation Service.

"Hurry, there went the game," "He who bathes among the crocodiles," and "Owl, crevice sitter" are from, respectively, B. F. Stefaniszyn, "The hunting songs of the Ambo," *African Studies* 10, 1951, p. 7; B. W. Vilakazi, "The conception and development of poetry," *Bantu Studies* 12, 1938, p. 119; S. K. L. Lekgothoane, "Praises of animals in Northern Sotho," *Bantu Studies* 12, 1938, p. 211. Reprinted with the permission of Witwatersrand University Press, Johannesburg, South Africa, publishers of *African Studies and Bantu Studies*.

"How shall I begin my songs," "The owl hooted and told," and "The water-bug is drawing," from *The American Indians and Their Music*, by Francis Densmore, published by Women's Press, 1926.

"The poor little bee," from *American Indian Love Lyrics*, published by Macmillan.

"The spirit walking," from *American Primitive Music*, by Frederick Burton, published by Moffat, Yard & Co., 1909.

"Song of the Fisherman," "The squirrel in his shirt," from Vol. 2 and Vol. 36 of the *American Anthropologist*; "The magpie! The magpie!" from "Navaho Gambling Songs," by Washington Matthews, which appeared in the *American Anthropologist* (Vol. 2, No. 1). Reprinted with the permission of the publisher.

"Song to Bring Fair Weather" and "Sing your song looking" appeared in *Nootka and Quileote Music*, by Francis Densmore. From *Bureau of American Ethnology Bulletin No. 124* (1939). Reprinted by permission of the Smithsonian Institution.

"A joyful chant," from *Oceania*, Vol. xv, No. 3, March 1945. Reprinted with the permission of the University of Sydney.

"Here on my breast," from *Ojibwa Songs*, by H. H. Schoolcraft.

"By the sandy water I breathe," "A low range of mountains," and "Two Rain Songs" appeared in "Papago Music," by Francis Densmore. From *Bureau of American Ethnology Bulletin No. 90* (1929). Reprinted by permission of the Smithsonian Institution.

"It is there that our hearts" appeared in "Pawnee Music." From *Bureau of American Ethnology Bulletin No. 93* (1929). Reprinted by permission of the Smithsonian Institution.

"The Mother's Song," from *Peter Freuchen's Book of the Eskimos*, edited by Dagmar Freuchen. Reprinted with the permission of The World Publishing Co. and Arthur Barker Ltd.

"The noise of passing feet" first appeared in *Poetry*. Reprinted by permission of the editor.

"Sing me a song, a song of death," from *Primitive Man as Philosopher*, by Paul Radin, published by Dover Publications, Inc.

"The black turkey-gobbler," from *Putnam Anniversary Volume*, by Goddard, N.Y. 1909.

"Moon O mother moon," "My heart is all happy," "Sleep, sleep, little one, close your eyes," "Daughter of the woman with a low brow," and "O Sun, O Sun Death comes," from *Primitive Song* by C. M. Bowra. Reprinted with the permission of The World Publishing Co. and Weidenfeld & Nicolson Ltd.

"My arms, they wave high," from the *Report of the Canadian Arctic Expedition, 1913-1918*, Vol. xiv, Ottawa, 1925.

"I arise from rest," "There is joy in feeling," "When I was young," from the *Report of the Fifth Thule Expedition, 1921-1924*, by Rasmussen.

"My bow, its lower part" and "From the skewer," from *Twelve Andamanese Songs*, by B. P. Kurtz. Reprinted with permission of the University of California Press.

"For want of gruel," from *The Veddas*, by C. G. and B. Z. Seligmann. Reprinted with the permission of Cambridge University Press.

"The Sky," translated by Kafu Hoh in *Voices of Ghana*. Reprinted with the permission of the Ministry of Information and Broadcasting, Ghana.

"I would I were a dragonfly," from *Voices on the Wind*, by Katherine Luomala. Reprinted with the permission of the copyright owner Bernice P. Bishop Museum, Honolulu, Hawaii.

"Over the sun-darkened river," from the *Western Aranda Rain Song of Kaporilja*, collected and translated by T. G. H. Strehlow.

"Peruvian Dance Song," from *The Winged Serpent*, by Margot Astrov. Reprinted with the permission of the John Day Company, Inc.

"Duck, you are merely boasting" and "The rain showers down," from *Yoruba Poetry*, collected by Bakare Gbadamdsi and Ulli Beirer. Published by Black Orpheus, General Publications Section, Ministry of Education, Ibadan, Nigeria.

I would like to take this opportunity to thank the New York Public Library, Museum of Primitive Art, Museum of Natural History, Bishop Museum, British Museum, Brooklyn Museum, and the Library of Congress for allowing me to make use of their extensive research facilities.

Thanks is also due to Charlene Slivnick for assisting with the typing of the manuscript in the early stages of this project; to William McMorris, my excellent editor; and my wife, Nancy, who forever encouraged me with her deep interest and enthusiasm for the poetry and art of primitive peoples.

To the makers of these songs,
who, though separate in their ways,
sing together
of the earth.

In the dry barren desert of the Kalahari in South Africa, the Bushman has lived for thousands of years. A story is told of how the Bushman's wife will stand at night—holding her child up to the sky—and sing to the stars, asking them to take the heart of her child and in return give him a heart of a star. She is singing because she believes that the stars are great hunters—and what she wants for her child is the heart of a hunter.

This book is a collection of songs from primitive peoples of the world, who, like the Bushman, must hunt in order to live, and in living must sing. It is a book meant to be read for the beauty of its poetry as well as the story it tells of a people. A people who are able to survive with the simplest of means—a people, outwardly having few possessions, but whose imaginations hold beliefs rich in the meaning of the stars, the moon, the sun, and the earth. A people, like all of us, answering their instinct to love, worship, laugh, cry, and be struck with awe. It is the story of a way of life lived close to the earth where the wind and the rain, darkness and light are precious threads in the fabric of each day. It is the songs themselves—sung in celebration, in lament, in hope, in prayer—composed at every turn of the day to express some event and feeling. Whether it be the hunting of food, the coming of day, the falling of rain—or seeing a lizard, an owl, a crab, a hummingbird—or praying to the moon and the sun, or telling of love, the fear of death, the strangeness of night—nothing is too unimportant to be the subject and reason for a song.

Introduction

For some of these people, songs are the only things they own. They are composed by themselves or a song-maker for everyone in the family and tribe to use. Each song is passed from generation to generation, repeated over and over again until it becomes worn, and then a new song will be composed.

An example of this is when the Eskimos hold a festival for the soul of whale as the great prize of the huntsman. Each festival would have a new song composed especially for it. The men gather together in silence—waiting for the words and melody to come forth and, "while everyone is trying hard to think fair thoughts, songs are born in the minds of men, rising like bubbles from the depths—bubbles seeking breath in which to burst."

Many of the people whose words are in this book are no longer wandering the earth. Their tribes have been scattered or absorbed into the onrush of other cultures—their customs forgotten and they themselves killed by men hungry in the greed for land. All we have left, in some instances, are a few pieces of art and the words of their songs. Much of what you will read here was taken down by scientists and scholars interested in having a record of these vanishing cultures. These scholars, some of whom were sensitive to the beauty of various songs of different cultures, made every effort to translate from the primitive languages the meaning and intent of each song.

In putting together a book of this type, I felt and saw certain things which were not obvious to me at the start. It became clear that primitive peoples had and still have secrets about living, which our "civilized" cultures could learn from. Part of their secret is that they have not broken their hold on the rhythms of the earth—they live with and alongside the ever-changing weather, they are sensitive to the ways of animals and creatures, they understand the solemnity of ritual—they are alive to the natural world in a way that we, over the centuries, have lost.

One also sees that their songs—(which is *their* literature)—come from the same need we have to express experience and feeling, to fashion beauty and form out of the elements of life and to leave something of our personalities behind for those who follow us.

These songs, so rich in poetic thought, still ring true today because they speak not only of the world of primitive men—but of our world and experience. They echo moods and thoughts which in the corners of our memories we have long since forgotten. They bring attention to sights and sounds that in the beginning of our time on earth we accepted and understood. But most important, they sing of the joys, fears, dreams and cares of humanity as a whole—and it is in this singing, in these words, that we may renew our link to a people, who, from the earth, must sing.

—Richard Lewis
Jan. 1967

Out Of The Earth I Sing

The White Light Of Morning

At the time when the earth became hot
At the time when the heavens turned about
At the time when the sun was darkened
To cause the moon to shine
The time of the rise of the Pleiades
The slime, this was the source of the earth
The source of the darkness that made the darkness
The source of the night that made night
The intense darkness, the deep darkness
Darkness of the sun, darkness of the night
Nothing but night.

—HAWAIIAN
(Pacific)

2

SONG OF THE SUN AND MOON

The first man holds it in his hands,
He holds the sun in his hands.
In the center of the sky, he holds it in his hands.
As he holds it in his hands, it starts upward.

The first woman holds it in her hands,
She holds the moon in her hands.
In the center of the sky, she holds it in her hands.
As she holds it in her hands, it starts upward.

The first man holds it in his hands,
He holds the sun in his hands.
In the center of the sky, he holds it in his hands.
As he holds it in his hands, it starts downward.

The first woman holds it in her hands,
She holds the moon in her hands.
In the center of the sky, she holds it in her hands.
As she holds it in her hands, it starts downward.

—NAVAHO
(North America)

It is there that our hearts are set,
In the expanse of the heavens.

—PAWNEE
(North America)

Moon, O mother moon, O mother moon,
Mother of living things,
Hear our voice, O mother moon!
O mother moon, O mother moon,
Keep away the spirits of the dead,
Hear our voice, O mother moon,
O mother moon! O mother moon!

—GABON PYGMIE
(Africa)

SONG OF THE SKY LOOM

O our Mother the Earth, O our Father the Sky,
Your children are we, and with tired backs
We bring you the gifts you love.
Then weave for us a garment of brightness;
May the warp be the white light of morning,
May the weft be the red light of evening,
May the fringes be the falling rain,
May the border be the standing rainbow.
Thus weave for us a garment of brightness,
That we may walk fittingly where birds sing,
That we may walk fittingly where grass is green,
O our Mother the Earth, O our Father the Sky.

—TEWA
(North America)

A PRAYER

Sun, my relative
Be good coming out
Do something good for us.

Make me work,
So I can do anything in the garden
I hoe, I plant corn, I irrigate.

You, sun, be good going down at sunset
We lay down to sleep I want to feel good.

While I sleep you come up.
Go on your course many times.
Make good things for us men.

Make me always the same as I am now.

—HAVASUPAI
(North America)

The noise of passing feet
On the prairie—
Is it men or gods
Who come out of the silence?

—CHIPPEWA
(North America)

HYMN TO THE SUN

The fearful night sinks
trembling into the depth
before your lightning eye
and the rapid arrows
from your fiery quiver.
With sparking blows of light
you tear her cloak
the black cloak lined with fire
and studded with gleaming stars—
with sparking blows of light
you tear the black cloak.

—FANG
(Africa)

The voice that beautifies the land!
The voice above,
The voice of the thunder,
Among the dark clouds
Again and again it sounds,
The voice that beautifies the land.

The voice that beautifies the land!
The voice below,
The voice of the grasshopper,
Among the flowers and grasses
Again and again it sounds,
The voice that beautifies the land.

—NAVAHO
(North America)

The owl hooted and told of the morning star,
He hooted again and told of the dawn.

—YUMA
(North America)

THE LITTLE FLY

Brother little fly flies around and looks at the sun.

—YAQUI
(North America)

THE EAGLE

The sun's rays
Lie along my wings
And stretch beyond their tips.

—PAPAGO
(North America)

13

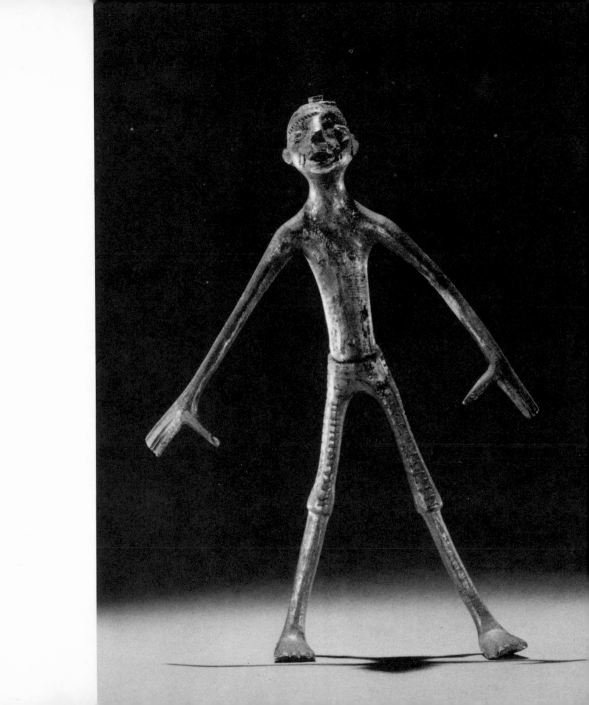

The magpie! The magpie! Here underneath
In the white of his wings are the footsteps of morning.
It dawns! It dawns!

—TEWA
(North America)

A low range of mountains, towards them I am running
From the top of these mountains I will see the dawn.

—PAPAGO
(North America)

15

SONG TO BRING FAIR WEATHER

You, whose day it is, make it beautiful.
Get out your rainbow colors,
So it will be beautiful.

—NOOTKA
(North America)

The black turkey gobbler, under the East, the middle of his tail;
    toward us it is about to dawn.
The black turkey gobbler, the tips of his beautiful tail;
    above us the dawn whitens.
The black turkey gobbler, the tips of his beautiful tail;
    above us the dawn becomes yellow.
The sunbeams stream forward, dawn boys,
    with shimmering shoes of yellow;
On top of the sunbeams that stream toward us they are dancing.
At the East the rainbow moves forward, dawn maidens,
    with shimmering shoes and shirts of yellow dance over us.
Beautifully over us it is dawning.
Above us among the mountains the herbs are becoming green;
Above us on the tops of the mountains the herbs are becoming yellow.
Above us among the mountains, with shoes of yellow
    I go around the fruits and herbs that shimmer.
Above us among the mountains, the shimmering fruits
    with shoes and shirts of yellow are bent toward him.
On the beautiful mountains above it is daylight.

—MESCALERO APACHE
(North America)

I arise from rest with movements swift
As the beat of the raven's wings
I arise
To meet the day.
My face is turned from the dark of night
To gaze at the dawn of day,
Now whitening in the sky.

—ESKIMO
(Arctic)

What is this
     I promise you?
The skies shall be bright and clear for you
This is what I promise you.

—CHIPPEWA
(North America)

I the singer stand on high on the yellow rushes;
Let me go forth with noble songs and laden with
flowers.

—AZTEC
(Central America)

DANCE OF THE ANIMALS

I throw myself to the left,
I turn myself to the right,
I am the fish
Who glides in the water, who glides,
Who twists himself, who leaps.
Everything lives, everything dances, everything sings.

The bird flies,
Flies, flies, flies,
Goes, comes back, passes,
Mounts, hovers, and drops down.
I am the bird.
Everything lives, everything dances, everything sings.

The monkey, from bough to bough,
Runs, leaps, and jumps,
With his wife, with his little one,
His mouth full, his tail in the air:
This is the monkey, this is the monkey.
Everything lives, everything dances, everything sings.

—PYGMIE
(Africa)

We Pray For Children

Throughout the world
Who is there like little me!
Who is like me!
I can touch the sky,
I touch the sky indeed!

—WINNEBAGO
(North America)

We pray that the beetles appear
That they may be very many.

We pray for mushrooms
That they may be very many.

We pray for children
That they may be very many.

—SEGADA
(Philippines)

My children, my children,
The wind makes my head feathers sing—
The wind makes my head feathers sing—
My children, my children.

—ARAPAHO
(North America)

LULLABY

Baby swimming down the river:
Little driftwood legs,
Little rabbit legs.

–KIOWA
(North America)

Why dost thou weep, my child?
The sky is bright; the sun is shining;
Why dost thou weep?
Go to thy father: he loves thee,
Go tell him why thou weepest.
What! Thou weepest still?
Thy father loves thee, I caress thee:
Yet still thou art sad.
Tell me, then, my child, why dost thou weep!

—BELENGI
(Africa)

Be still, my child,
Do you see those birds
In the tree?
If you cry,
A little bird
Is going to carry you off.

—BASARI
(Africa)

29

CRADLE SONG FOR A BOY

Let me shoot a small bird for my younger brother.
Let me spear a small trout for my sister.

—TLINGIT
(North America)

When I am a man, then I shall be a hunter, O father!
    Ya ha ha ha.
When I am a man, then I shall be a harpooner, O father!
    Ya ha ha ha.
When I am a man, then I shall be a canoebuilder, O father!
    Ya ha ha ha.
When I am a man, then I shall be a carpenter, O father!
    Ya ha ha ha.
When I am a man, then I shall be an artisan, O father!
    Ya ha ha ha.
That we may not be in want, O father!
    Ya ha ha ha.

—NORTHWEST COAST INDIAN
(North America)

31

Sing your song
Looking up at the sky.

—NOOTKA
(North America)

Be kind,
Do not steal,
Do not touch what belongs to another,
Leave all such alone,
Be kind.

—ABORIGINAL
(Australia)

My arms, they wave high in the air,
My hands, they flutter behind my back; they
    wave above my head like the wings
    of a bird.
Let me move my face, let me dance, let me
    shrug my shoulders, let me shake my body.
Let me fold my arms, let me crouch down,
Let me hold my hands under my chin.

—ESKIMO
(Arctic)

Every Living Creature

I SING FOR THE ANIMALS

Out of the earth
I sing for them,
A Horse nation
I sing for them.
Out of the earth
I sing for them,
The animals
I sing for them.

—TETON SIOUX
(North America)

How joyous his neigh!
Lo, the Turquoise horse of Jahano-ai,
How joyous his neigh!
There on precious hides outspread standeth he;
How joyous his neigh,
There on tips of fair fresh flowers feedeth he;
How joyous his neigh,
There of mingled waters holy drinketh he;
How joyous his neigh,
There he spurneth dust of glittering grains;
How joyous his neigh,
There in mist of sacred pollen hidden, all hidden, he;
How joyous his neigh,
There his offspring many grow and thrive for evermore;
How joyous his neigh!

—NAVAHO
(North America)

SONG OF THE BUTTERFLY

In the coming heat
    of the day
  I stood there.

      —CHIPPEWA
      (North America)

    Duck, you are merely boasting.
    You have born children.
    But you have no back to carry them!
    Duck, you are merely boasting.

        —YORUBA
        (Africa)

He who bathes among crocodiles,
The crocodiles will not attack him,
They care for his bubbles.

—ZULU
(Africa)

Sitting on the stone, O crab,
Move a little,
From the stone, O crab.
Let me plough the field, O crab,
Move a little,
From the stone, O crab.

—PULLAYAS OF KERALA
(India)

SONG OF THE FOUR LITTLE SHELL-ANIMALS

We are going to see the little crabs,
We hear that they leave piles of bubbles.

—QUILEUTE
(North America)

Owl, crevice-sitter
When it rains, where do you sit?

—SOTHO
(Africa)

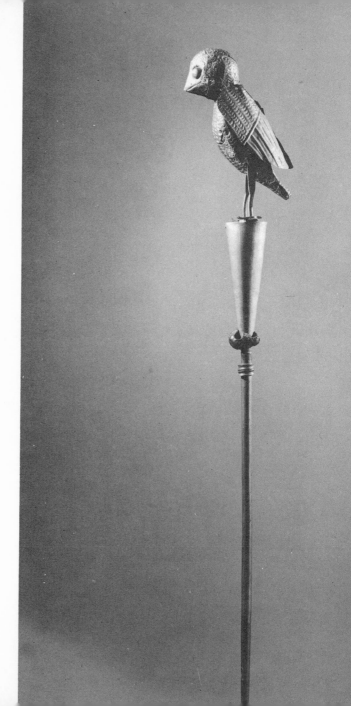

I would I were
A dragonfly exulting in the sunshine.

—POLYNESIAN
(Pacific)

LULLABY

Sleep, sleep, sleep!
In the trail the beetles
Carry each other on their back.
Sleep, sleep, sleep!

—ZUNI
(North America)

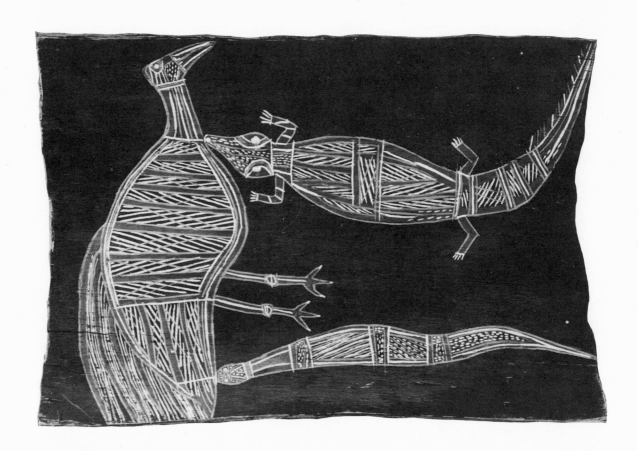

44

Paddling we saw that turtle; saw its eyes open,
    its flippers outstretched, as it floated.
Sea-water lapped at its shell, spreading across its back.

—ABORIGINAL
(Australia)

The buffalo goes with his head on high,
The bird is on his ear,
The flute of the buffalo
Sounds in the river.

—LANGO
(Africa)

There are the eagles crying, swooping from side to side,
Pecking in play at each other's feathers, their feathers falling;
Crying out and flashing there in the sun;
Soon in their nest there will be young eaglets.

—ABORIGINAL
(Australia)

Oh, oh!
The lizard lives on the thorn tree.
Oh, oh!
Oh, oh, the lizard lies on the thorn tree.
Oh, oh!
The lizard was lying on the thorn tree.

—BUSHMAN
(Africa)

47

Please don't kill my antelope,
My darling antelope.
My antelope is so poor,
My antelope is an orphan.

                    —BUSHMAN
                         (Africa)

SONG OF HUMMINGBIRD

. . . I am feeling very lonely away.
I am singing inside.
I am crying about myself.

                         —TLINGIT
                         (North America)

The poor little bee
  That lives in the tree
The poor little bee
  That lives in the tree
Has only one arrow
  In his quiver.

−K A - N I - G A
(North America)

The Grey quails were bunched
   together;
Coyote ran to look upon them.
The Blue quails were bunched
   together;
Coyote looked sidewise at them.

−P I M A
(North America)

PADDLING SONG

My dugout canoe goes
Swiftly down the river.
In every tree the monkeys
Are chattering and crying.
Oh, big jungle hunter,
Tell me of their trouble.

The little monkey broke his leg
So they all are crying.

Then band to your paddle,
Hunter of the river,
And tell the mother that
Her monkey-baby's crying:
The little monkey broke his leg.
They are all crying.

—BANTU
(Africa)

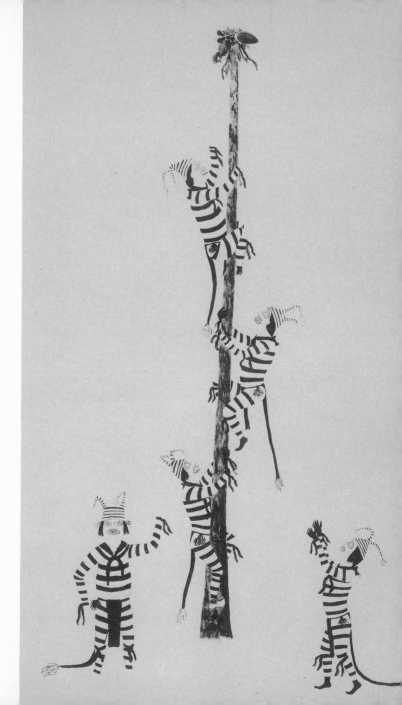

The squirrel in his shirt stands there,
The squirrel in his shirt stands there;
Slender, he stands up there; striped he stands
      up there.

—NAVAHO
(North America)

54

Cricket come back! You've left your drum behind,
and it is still sounding, Mr. Cricket!

–L A M B A
(Africa)

Because I am poor,
I pray for every living creature.

–K I O W A
(North America)

Something I've Killed

HUNTING PRAYER

I do not know
What will happen to me
Regarding food,
What will happen to me
Regarding food.
I do not know
What I shall do
To get something to eat.
Let us eat and become big.

—BUSHMAN
(Africa)

My bow, its lower part, I drew back,
My bow, its lower part.
Stooping, softly creeping,
Stooping, softly creeping.

—ANDAMANESE
(*India*)

HUNTING SONG

Something I've killed, and I lift up my
voice,
Something I've killed, and I lift up my
voice,
The mother buffalo I've killed, and I
lift up my voice,
Something I've killed, and I lift up my
voice.

—DAKOTA
(*North America*)

SONG OF THE FISHERMEN

O fish, come
And take your good food.
Do not send the little fish
To spoil the good food.
Better you come
And take the good food
With all your strength.

—MBUNDU
(Africa)

HUNTING SONG

Hurry, there went the game,
Hurry, there went the game,
The grass is trodden.

—AMBO
(Africa)

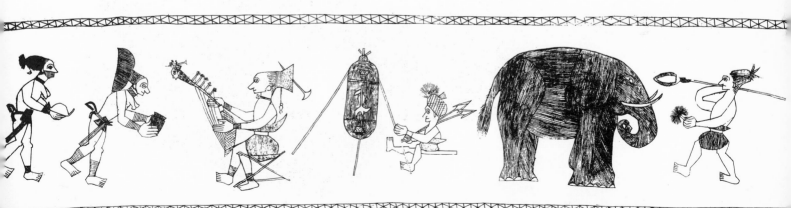

PRAYER TO THE MOON

Ho, my hand is this,
I shoot a springbok with my hand
By an arrow.

I will lie down,
I will kill an early springbok
Tomorrow.

Ho, moon lying there
Let me kill a springbok,
Tomorrow.

Let me eat a springbok;
With this arrow
Let me shoot a springbok;
With this arrow
Let me eat a springbok;
Let me eat, filling my body
In the night which is here;
Let me fill my body.

Ho, moon lying there,
I dig out ants food
Tomorrow
Let me eat it.
Ho, moon lying there,
You must look at this arrow
That I may shoot a springbok with it
    tomorrow.

           –BUSHMAN
           (Africa)

HUNTING SONG

Comes the deer to my singing,
Comes the deer to my song,
Comes the deer to my singing.

He, the blackbird, he am I,
Bird beloved of the wild deer,
Comes the deer to my singing.

From the Mountain Black
From the summit,
Down the trail, coming now, coming
Comes the deer to my singing.

Through the flower dewdrops
Coming, coming now,
Comes the deer to my singing.

Through the pollen, flower pollen
    Coming, coming now,
    Comes the deer to my singing.

Starting with his left forefoot,
Stamping, turns the frightened deer,
    Comes the deer to my singing.

    Quarry mine, blessed am I
    In the luck of the chase.
    Comes the deer to my singing.

    Comes the deer to my singing,
    Comes the deer to my song,
    Comes the deer to my singing.

                        —NAVAHO
                        (*North America*)

65

From the skewer O the blood O on my skin
     dripped down,
On my skin kept dripping down,
From the pig O on my skin kept
Dripping down, from the pig O on my skin kept
Dripping down, from the pig O on my skin kept.

                 —ANDAMANESE
                    (India)

The Voice Of The Thunders

New moon, come out, give water for us,
New moon, thunder down water for us,
New moon shake down water for us.

—BUSHMAN
(Africa)

THE SONG OF THE RAIN

Under the sun
The earth is dry
By the fire
Alone I cry
All day long
The earth cries
For the rain to come.
All night my heart cries
For my hunter to come
And take me away.

Oh! Listen to the wind,
You woman there;
The time is coming,
The rain is near.
Listen to your heart,
Your hunter is here.

—BUSHMAN
(Africa)

By the sandy water I breathe the odor of the sea,
From there the wind comes and blows over the world.
By the sandy water I breathe the odor of the sea,
From there the clouds come and the rain falls
     over the world.

          —PAPAGO
          (North America)

  Over the sun-darkened river sands calls the
     voice of the thunder, the voice of the
     thunder;

  From billowing storm-clouds calls the voice
     of the thunder, the voice of the thunder.

  A flash of lightning
  Shivers trees in pieces.

  The first storm-showers,
  The first storm-showers are pouring down
     in torrents, are pouring down in
     torrents.

          —ABORIGINAL
          (Australia)

FIRST SONG OF THE THUNDER

Thonah! Thonah!
There is the voice above
The voice of the thunder.
Within the dark cloud,
Again and again it sounds,
Thonah! Thonah!

Thonah! Thonah!
There is a voice below,
The voice of the grasshopper.
Among the plants,
Again and again it sounds,
Thonah! Thonah!

—NAVAHO
(North America)

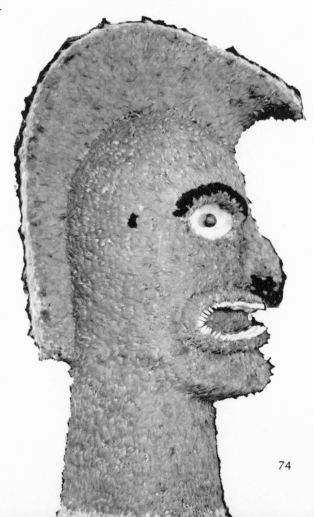

74

A cloud on top of Evergreen Mountain is singing,
A cloud on top of Evergreen Mountain is
      standing still,
It is raining and thundering up there,
It is raining here,
Under the mountain the corn tassels are shaking,
Under the mountain the horns of the child corn
      are glistening.

—PAPAGO
(North America)

76

This lizard, with body poised,
Watches the rain waters swirling past.

—ABORIGINAL
(Australia)

SONG OF THE THUNDERS

Sometimes
I go about pitying
myself
while I am carried by the wind
across the sky.

—CHIPPEWA
(North America)

The corn grows up.
The waters of the dark clouds drop, drop.
The rain descends.
The waters from the corn leaves drop, drop.
The rain descends.
The waters from the plants drop, drop.
The corn grows up.
The waters of the dark mists drop, drop.

—NAVAHO
(North America)

The rain showers down.
The earth is getting cool.
All the birds on the farm are crying:
Shee-ooo; shee-ooo; shee-ooo!

—YORUBA
(Africa)

In summer the rains come and the grass grows up.
That is the time that the deer has new horns.

—YAQUI
(North America)

A Whispered Word

A joyful chant,
A whispered word,
A meeting on the road.
A joyful glance,
A pert glance,
A painted face,
An admiring look,
A disdaining look,
A little tease,
A meeting on the road.
A joyful chant,
A whispered word,
A meeting on the road.

—TROBRIAND ISLANDS
(Pacific)

LOVE SONG

I walk alone.

—ZULU
(Africa)

For want of gruel or food, life will not depart;
Owing to cold or wind, life will not depart;
Owing to rain or dew, life will not depart.
If there be no wife, life will depart.

—VEDDA
(Ceylon)

The road looks longer as I go to meet her,
The stars seem to whisper,
The moon seems to welcome;
The rising sun says: I know you.

—AO NAGA
(India)

Waves, coming up against the rocks,
Breaking, shi! shi!
When the moon is high with its light on the
        waters;
Spring tide, tide flowing to the grass,
Breaking, shi! shi!
In its rough waters the young girls bathe.
Hear the sound which they make with their
        hands as they play!

—ABORIGINAL
(Australia)

All your young beauty is to me
Like a place where the new grass sways,
After the blessing of the rain,
Where the sun unveils its light.

—SOMALI
(Africa)

My heart is all happy,
My heart takes wing in singing,
Under the trees of the forest,
The forest our dwelling and our mother.
On my thread I have taken,
A little, a very little bird.
My heart is caught on the thread,
On the thread with the bird.

—PYGMY
(Africa)

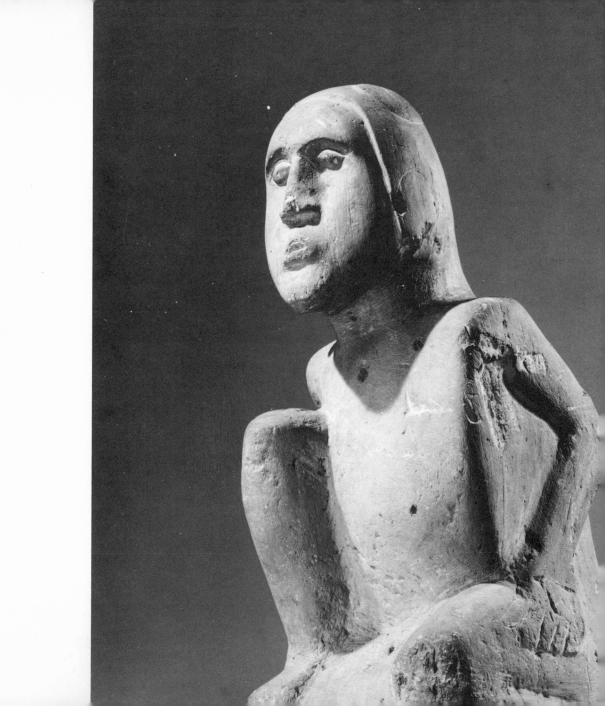

To this my song
Thou shalt sleep.
In the dead of night
I shall come.

–INCA
(South America)

A loon I thought it was
But it was
My love's
Splashing oar.

–CHIPPEWA
(North America)

If you become the moon, my love,
I'll be the light of the moon,
How close ever I'll follow you.

— FROM SONG OF RANGA
(India)

I shall be a swan and swim in your pond,
I shall be a fish and get caught in your net,
I shall be perspiration rolling down your body,
I shall be a fly and settle on your cheek.

— ASSAMESE
(India)

Like two doves we left my town,
we were two doves who flew from their nest.
In my town we were happy,
In my house we were happy,
like two doves we left my town.

Ay, what will I say now when they ask me
where is your little dove,
why do you return alone!
How shall I enter, alone, my town,
having left with my love
like two doves who flew from their nest?

—QUECHUA
(South America)

LEAVE-TAKING

Today is the day of my departure,
today I will not go, I will go tomorrow.
You may see me leave playing a flute of fly bone,
carrying for banner a spider web,
my drum will be an egg of an ant,
and my cap! my cap will be a hummingbird nest.

—QUECHUA
(South America)

The Night Comes Down

At the time that turned the heat of the earth,
At the time when the heavens turned and changed,
At the time when the light of the sun was subdued
To cause light to break forth,
At the time of the night of winter,
Then began the slime which established the earth,
The source of the deepest darkness;
Of the depth of the darkness, of the depth of the darkness,
Of the darkness of the sun, in the depth of night;
    It is night:
    Thus was night born.

—MAORI
(New Zealand)

The water bug is drawing the shadows of evening
toward him across the water.

—YUMA
(North America)

MEDICINE SONG

How shall I begin my songs
In the blue night that is settling?

In the great night my heart will go out,
Toward me the darkness comes rattling.
In the great night my heart will go out.

—NAVAHO
(North America)

Blue evening falls,
Blue evening falls,
Nearby, in every direction.
It sets the corn tassels trembling.

—PAPAGO
(North America)

Sleep brings pearl necklaces, do not cry, baby,
Sleep brings sweet dishes, do not cry, baby,
Do not cry, baby,
It is time, you must sleep now,
As the fish sleeps in the pool.

—MIKIRIS
(India)

There is joy in
Feeling the warmth
Come to the great world
And seeing the sun
Follow its old footprints
In the summer night.

There is fear in
Feeling the cold
Come to the great world
And seeing the moon
—Now new moon, now full moon—
Follow its old footprints
In the winter night.

—ESKIMO
(Arctic)

POLAR STAR

The circuit of earth which you see,
The scattering of stars in the sky which you see,
All that is the place for my hair.

—WINTU
(North America)

The moon cannot fight
Sun leave him alone.
The moon cannot fight
Sun leave him alone!

The moon gives the earth his good light.
Come and eat beancakes with us at midnight.
Thief! Thief with the goggle eye!

—YORUBA
(Africa)

Mother moon, bless baby,
Let him live a hundred thousand years,
Moon, give him milk and basi.
Let it come swaying this way,
Let it come swaying this way,
And straight into baby's mouth.

—MAIKAL HILLS
(India)

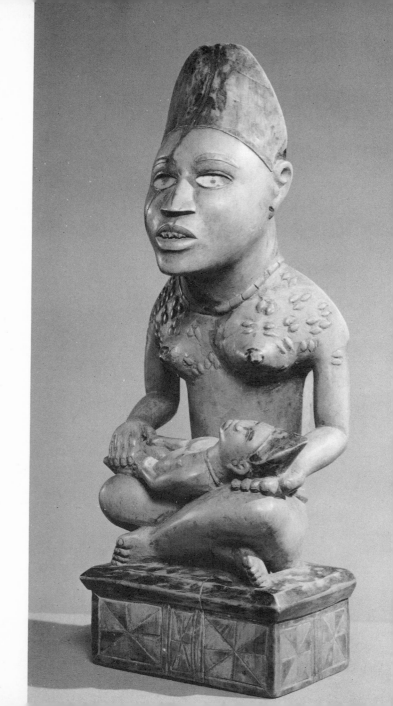

DARKNESS SONG

We wait in the darkness!
Come, all ye who listen,
Help in our night journey:
Now no sun is shining;
Now no star is glowing;
Come show us the pathway:
The night is not friendly;
She closes her eyelids;
The moon has forgot us,
We wait in the darkness!

—IROQUOIS
(North America)

The wind was once a man
Who wandered on the earth,
Now he is a bird
Who flies high.

He became a bird who flies,
Who bites our skin:
A bird we feel, a bird we hear
A bird we cannot see.

The wind-bird seeks food,
The wind-bird hunts,
When it has eaten its prey
It flies home again.

When he hunts, the sky rumbles,
The sand flies around;
When he sleeps the sky rests—
And then we sleep, too.

—BUSHMAN
(Africa)

At night may I roam
Against the winds may I roam
At night may I roam
When the owl is hooting
May I roam.

At dawn may I roam
Against the winds may I roam
At dawn may I roam
When the crow is calling
May I roam.

—TETON SIOUX
(North America)

THE SKY

The sky at night is like a big city
where beasts and men abound,
but never once has anyone
killed a fowl or a goat,
and no bear has ever killed a prey.
There are no accidents; there are no losses.
Everything knows its way.

—EWE
(Africa)

When a man's body is young
At night he gives up his sleep
And sings, and sings!

—MARQUESAS ISLANDS
(Pacific)

110

Sleep, sleep, little one, close your eyes, sleep, little one!
The night comes down, the hour has come, tomorrow it will be day.
Sleep, sleep, little one! On your closed eyes day has fled.
You are warm. You have drunk, sleep, sleep, little one!
Sleep, tomorrow you will be big, you will be strong.
Sleep, tomorrow you will take the bow and the knife.
Sleep, you will be strong, you will be straight, and I bent.
Sleep, tomorrow it is you, but it is mother always.

—GABON PYGMIE
(Africa)

The spirit walking in the sky takes care of us.

—OJIBWAY
(North America)

O, you are like the tender cotton worm
O, go to sleep, my tiny bubble.

—MANIPURIES
(India)

THE MOTHER'S SONG

It is so still in the house.
There is a calm in the house;
The snowstorm wails out there,
And the dogs are rolled up with snouts under the tail.
My little boy is sleeping on the ledge,
On his back he lies, breathing through his open mouth.
His little stomach is bulging round—
Is it strange if I start to cry with joy?

—ESKIMO
(Arctic)

113

114

Oh my sun, my Moon!
where are you rising,
where do you give light, becoming morning?
To that bay I will go.

Oh my Sun, my Moon!
as long as you are there
I weep in this growing darkness,
waiting in so much night.

Oh my Sun, my Moon!
where do you give light, becoming morning?
By that bay, by that ridge of the mountain
I will return, I will return.

—QUECHA
(South America)

115

A Long Journey

DEATH SONG OF A SONG MAKER

All my life
I have been seeking
Seeking!

–YOKUT
(North America)

When I was young,
every day was as a beginning
of some new thing,
and every evening ended
with the glow of the next day's dawn.

—ESKIMO
(Arctic)

WAR SONG

Here on my breast have I bled!
See-see! there are fighting scars!
Mountains tremble at my yell!
I strike for life!

—OJIBWAY
(*North America*)

LAST SONG OF SITTING BULL

A warrior
I have been.
Now
It is all over.
A hard time
I have.

—TETON SIOUX
   (North America)

ON WEALTH

I am rich
And I shall die;
You are poor
And you will die.

—MENDE
(Africa)

Poor fellow me,
Poor fellow me,
My country,
It gave me,

All that I see,
Gifts that I see,
All that I see,
Poor fellow me.

Once I was gay,
Once I was gay,
Once I was gay,
Poor fellow me.
Then came the day,
I went away,
Now I am grey,
Poor fellow me.

Now I'm alone,
Now I'm alone,
Now I'm alone,
Poor fellow me.
Nothing I own,
Spirit has flown,
Poor fellow me.

So let me die,
Peaceful I lie,
Let my shade fly.
Poor fellow me
Poor fellow me.

—ABORIGINAL
(*Australia*)

124

FAREWELL TO THE WARRIORS

Come
      it is time for you to depart
We are going on a long journey.

–CHIPPEWA
(North America)

I am a wanderer, I shall die stretched out.

—LAMBA
(North America)

We only came to sleep,
We only came to dream,
It is not true, it is not true
That we came to live upon earth.

We are changed into the spring grass;
Our hearts will grow green again
And they will open their petals,
But our body is like a rose tree,
It puts forth flowers and then withers.

—AZTEC
(Mexico)

Sing me a song, a song of death,
That I may guide it by the hand.
Sing me a song of the underworld.
Sing me a song, a song of death,
That I may walk to the underworld!

Thus speaks the underworld to me,
The underworld speaks thus:
"O beautiful it feels in the grave,
O lovely is the underworld!
But yet no palm wine can you drink."
Therefore I take you by the hand
And journey to the underworld.

—EWE
(*Africa*)

The day we die
Then the wind comes
To wipe us out,
The traces of our feet.
The wind creates dust
Which covers
The traces that were
Where we had walked,
For otherwise
It would be
As if we were
Still alive.
That is why it is the wind
That comes
To wipe out
The traces of our feet.

—BUSHMAN
(*Africa*)

130

PERUVIAN DANCE SONG

Wake up, woman,
Rise up, woman,
In the middle of the street
A dog howls.

May the death arrive,
May the dance arrive,

Comes the dance
You must dance,
Comes the death
You can't help it!

Ah! what a chill,
Ah! what a wind. . . .

—AYACUCHO
(*South America*)

When you have gone
We shall kiss your footprints
In the grass.

—BORNEO
(Pacific)

132

ON THE DEATH OF A WIFE

Daughter of the woman with a low brow, my
        companion,
Come and kiss me!
When will you arise and speak to me?
My companion is dumb and silent.
Instruct me then in singing
That I may help you to sing!
Arise, and let us look for caterpillars!
Arise and let us dig up wild onions!
Like one who could now arise, you lie there.
Cease to sleep, and arise!
Arise and kiss me!

                       —DAMA
                       (Africa)

O Sun, O Sun
Death comes, the end arrives,
The tree falls and dies.
O Sun, O Sun,
The child is born in his mother's womb.
Death saw, man saw, the Sun saw.
Sun, O Sun, O Sun.

—GABON PYGMIE
(Africa)

My flowers shall not perish
Nor shall my chants cease
They spread, they scatter.

—AZTEC
(Mexico)

My music
    Reaches
      To the sky.

    —CHIPPEWA
(North America)

I came from under the earth;
I part the bamboo leaves before me,
  I look to the heights,
I face two red clouds;
  They make me weep,
  If they were nearer
That would be the color of my song.

—MELANESIAN
(Pacific)

All things of earth have an end, and in the midst
of the most joyous lives, the breath falters, they
fall, they sink into the ground.

—AZTEC
(Mexico)

THE BEAUTIFUL

Above, above
The birds flying.
Below, below,
The flowers on the earth.

In the mountains, the mountains,
The trees growing.
In the ocean, the ocean,
The fish of the sea.

Here ends my song,
The beautiful world.

—HAWAIIAN
(Pacific)

139

Index of First Lines

Thanks are due to the following museums for allowing material from their collections to be reproduced in this anthology:

AMERICAN MUSEUM OF NATURAL HISTORY

Cover   Clay head. Veracruz, Mexico.
Page 4   Cast bronze. Dahomey, Africa.
Page 12   Design from an Indian bowl. Southwest United States.
Page 14   Cast bronze. Dahomey, Africa.
Page 24   Clay figure. Oaxaca, Mexico.
Page 28   Pottery dog and baby. Mexico.
Page 32   Bronze with paint. Togo border, Gold Coast, Africa.
Page 36   Vase. Oaxaca, Mexico.
Page 38   Vessel. Mexico.
Page 52   Indian painting by Alfonso Roybal. New Mexico.
Page 60–61   Pictographs on ivory. Congo, Africa.
Page 64–65   Deer by Aqwa Pi. Arizona.
Page 72   Cast bronze. Dahomey, Africa.
Page 86   Tapa cloth. Tahiti.
Page 94   Carving, Eskimo. Arctic.
Page 98   Las Remojadas sculpture. Veracruz, Mexico.
Page 126   Jar. Mexico.

BRITISH MUSEUM

Page 8   Bark painting. Aboriginal, Australia.
Page 66   Bronze. Benin, Nigeria, Africa.
Page 79   Cave painting. Africa.
Page 84   African sculpture.
Page 116   Mask. Benin, Nigeria, Africa.
Page 118   Figure. Africa.
Page 124   Wood carving. Africa.
Page 130–131   Masks. Africa.
Page 132   Mask. Africa.
Page 136   Aztec stone mask. Mexico.

THE BROOKLYN MUSEUM

Page 18   Mohave Indian pottery doll. Arizona.
Page 20   Female figure of wood. Bambala, Congo, Africa.

AUSTRALIAN MUSEUM

Page 50   Aboriginal bark painting. Australia.
Page 91   Aboriginal bark painting. Australia.

BERNICE P. BISHOP MUSEUM, HONOLULU, HAWAII

Page 74   Mask. Hawaii.

HELEN HARTMAN

Page 80   Maori carving. New Zealand.

THE OHIO HISTORICAL SOCIETY, OHIO STATE MUSEUM

Page xvi   Mica ornament. Hopewell Mounds, Ohio.
Page 122   Copper ornament. Mound City, Ohio.

FROM THE TRIBAL ART OF INDIA BY VERRIER ELWIN
PUBLISHED BY OXFORD UNIVERSITY PRESS

Page 108   Group of figures. Koraput District, Orissa, India.

ALEXANDER TURNBALL LIBRARY

Page 96   Maori cave painting. New Zealand.
Page 110   Maori pictograph. New Zealand.